D1132409

Comedy Around the Corral

Stu Campbell
Illustrations by R. Loren Schmidt

ISBN 978-0-9675164-5-5

Cover and text design by D.K. Luraas

Printed and bound in the United States of America

Contents

Megan and Mandy 1

Hunting Camp 7

Is Smaller Better? 15

Protection 25

Projecting an Image 31

Riding Herd 37

A Big Mistake 45

Making Money 49

A Day Off 53

Splitting Tips 57

Scar 63

Looks Ain't Everything 69

Missing Horses 75

"Details" 81

Old Friends 87

Still Embarrassed 93

How to Tell When a Cowboy is Lying 99

Megan and Mandy

Megan and Mandy came to work for us the summer season of 2008. They were both pretty green in regards to their horse experience, but they paid attention during our training sessions and they learned fast. They were willing and able to accept responsibility, and they applied what they learned to their job duties.

It was a real pleasure to work with them and everyone else on the crew that summer. Megan and Mandy were anxious to learn every aspect of the rental horse business that summer. I had even started them on the particulars of managing the office—answering the phone and making reservations. I would periodically quiz them on how to handle unexpected situations should they arise. They handled my little quiz sessions quite well, even though I would often throw them some preposterous situations. We had a lot of fun and some good laughs doing this.

Consequently, I was really pleased when they came back to work in 2009. We had set up an internship program, whereby they could receive college credit for their work in addition to their monthly salaries. We provided room and board, so they could pretty well save all the money they made and have a sizeable amount of cash to go back to school with in the fall.

I was tremendously pleased to have Megan and Mandy back as I sized up the other members of our crew. They were largely inexperienced, slow or lazy—I haven't figured out which, and exhibited a general "I don't care" attitude. Megan and Mandy with a year's experience would be a great help with this crew and a great help to me.

Both girls were in their early twenties: Megan was already twenty-one and Mandy due to turn twenty-one in July. They were both cute—even good-looking. I used to tell them that, "If I were twenty years younger, well, I'd still be twenty years too old for you!"

They'd just laugh, and give me a patented answer like, "You're not too old for us!"

I would generally reply, "My daddy always told me it was best to do business with an old, established firm!"

We teased a lot like that, and it was a lot of fun.

It is my custom to get up in the morning, go to the kitchen, start the coffee, and then go down to unlock the barn and corrals. By the time I'd get back to the kitchen, the coffee was done and I could get a big cup, sit on the porch of the bunkhouse, drink my coffee, have a smoke, and watch the sun come up.

Early in the spring I could watch the wildlife come down, and in the fall I could watch the elk and listen to their bugling. The mornings were the best, even though I was kinda disappointed that the cook didn't get up and make the coffee. The sound of my boots on the kitchen porch would generally wake up the cook. But as long as I made the coffee, I made a rule that

no one could have any coffee until I filled my cup. I didn't have much trouble enforcing this rule—most of the help tried to sleep in as long as they could, barely getting up in time for breakfast.

One morning, I was enjoying my coffee on the porch when the peace and quiet of the morning was shattered with frantic cries, "Stu! Stu!"

It was Megan. She was coming out of the girl's bunkhouse, buttoning up her shirt and pulling up her pants at the same time as best she could.

"Stu! Come here! We need you!" There was a note of urgency in her voice. "Hurry! We need you!"

I didn't know what to expect! Surely these girls hadn't taken my funning seriously!

"What's goin' on?"

"Mandy needs you!"

"How come?"

"She's got a tick in her ear!"

Mandy came out of the bunkhouse, fully dressed, and showed me her visitor.

My first thought was to get my lighter and burn the tick out, but ears are kinda sensitive, and I didn't want to set Mandy's hair on fire.

"Do you have some tweezers?" I asked.

"Yes," Megan replied.

"Get 'em an' bring 'em out here."

I didn't want to go in the girl's bunkhouse because the other girls were getting up and getting dressed.

Megan returned with the tweezers.

"This is going to require some major surgery," I said. "If it doesn't work, we'll probably just have to cut your ear off, Mandy!"

"Very funny, Stu." Mandy was very matter of fact. She was concerned, but not excited.

Carefully, I got the tick out. It hadn't embedded itself deeply, and it was fairly simple to get it intact. I put it on the porch rail and scrutinized it carefully to make sure I hadn't left any part of it in Mandy's ear. It was whole, and both Megan and Mandy crowded in close as I set it on fire.

"It won't be bothering anyone else now," I said as I watched it shrivel up in the flame. "Anything else I can do for you this morning, girls? You know, I can do a lot of things you don't even know about! Truthfully, it's only modesty that prohibits me from tellin' you of all the talents that I actually do have!"

"We know, Stu, we know."

"Keep an eye on that, Mandy. If you start to feel funny or strange, let me know. We'll take you to the Doc an' have you checked out for that Rocky Mountain Spotted Fever. An' Megan, don't come out of the bunkhouse again until you're fully dressed! You might give this ol' man a heart attack!"

I winked at the girls as they smiled and went to breakfast. I finished my coffee, relieved that the emergency wasn't more serious.

I have come to think of the girls as my little nieces, and have the highest regards for them.

Hunting Camp

I never really cared for the fall hunting camps—there was a lot of work involved. The work didn't bother me so much, what really bothered me was the cold. I didn't like sleeping in a tent on the cold ground, getting up in the morning and having to start a fire just to get some heat. It always took a while for the fire to get going and I didn't like standing there trying to get warm.

I learned early in hunting camp to cover the wood the night before just in case it rained or snowed during the night. I was always miserably cold while trying to get a fire started with wet wood. It only took one experience to learn this lesson. The firewood would always be covered each night, even if it didn't look like it would rain or snow.

At the higher elevations, where the elk hunters preferred to camp and where the chances of bagging their game were better, it always got cold at night. It would warm up during the day, unless it rained or snowed, and I was constantly either over-dressed or under-dressed. I was always uncomfortable.

I also found it difficult to provide for the hunters. If I was the only wrangler or guide with a bunch of hunters, it was a lot of work to set up camp, take care of the horses, gather firewood, cook, and then take the hunters out. Then, if they got something, I had to go get it, clean it, and bring it back to camp.

Sometimes, the hunters would pitch in by gathering some firewood, or help with the horses, but generally they weren't much help. However, I appreciated their efforts when they tried. The small groups—one or two—were the best; larger groups of four or five were more difficult. With big groups, nine or ten or more, I would generally have another guide or two and a cook.

The cook was most appreciated. I get real tired of my own cooking, and while it ain't so bad, it ain't all that good! My own cooking lingers closer to the bad side rather than the good side. Consequently, the cook became the most respected person in camp, in my opinion.

For all the misery in hunting camp, there are some really good times and a lot of fun can be had.

We were setting up camp for a large group and an extended hunt. During a break, the cook went to a gunny sack and pulled out a paper bag with some plastic items in it, got a screwdriver, a hammer, and a wood chisel, and walked to a tree.

He began carving out a rectangular shape in the bark of a pine tree, about a foot above the ground. Curious, I walked over to where he was working.

"What you making, Cookie? You're not fixin' up supper with them bark shavin's, are you?"

"No! No, nitwit," replied the cook. "I'm fixin' to have some fun with these hunters. They've hunted with us before an' they're a fun bunch."

I watched as the cook completed his carving, then attached an electrical outlet to the tree. When it was secured, it looked just like an outlet on a wall. He also hung a mirror on the tree. Then he went to another tree and carved out a similar shape, about shoulder high. In this carving he placed an electrical wall switch. His work completed, he went back to cooking the noon meal.

We finished setting up camp, which consisted of three or four sleeping tents, a cook tent, and a tent for the wranglers and guides, then went back to the ranch. The hunters were due to show up the next day, and the following day we were to pack them and their gear into camp.

These guys really knew how to camp. They had all sorts of cots, chaise lounges, and gadgets to make their hunting experience more comfortable. They needed an extra pack horse just to carry their beer and liquor. I could tell as I packed a horse, that this was not going to be a "roughing it" experience.

By the time we got the horses loaded, it was getting pretty close to noon. The cook had gone ahead to start the evening meal. It would be a three- or four-hour ride to camp and we would get there just in time for supper.

The ride to camp was uneventful, although we had to stop frequently as the hunters saw a few elk on the far hillsides and wanted to look them over. When we reached camp the hunters were obviously relieved. Four hours in the saddle can be tough if a feller isn't used to riding. I could tell by watching the riders that some of them weren't having a very good time.

The hunters couldn't wait while we unpacked the horses. As soon as the chaise lounges and easy chairs were unloaded, they were occupied! Groans and sighs of relief accompanied the hunters as they settled into their seats and opened up their beers.

They seemed perfectly content to relax and wait a few minutes for supper.

I hobbled the horses and turned them loose. They knew the area and wouldn't stray far. They'd all be in camp looking for their grain in the morning. As I returned to camp, I had the thought, This looks more like a sidewalk sale than a hunting camp! Chaise lounges and easy chairs were strung about in a haphazard fashion. There were a few empty beer cans beside a lot of the furniture.

I was the last one to get supper that night. As the cook surveyed the hunters while they were eating, he made an announcement.

"We have added some improvements to our camp this year! The first one is Stu."

I was unprepared for this unrehearsed introduction, and raised a hand in recognition. I had already met the hunters at the ranch when they arrived.

"I don't know if Stu is really an improvement or not," continued the cook, "but we'll find out.

"We also moved the latrine downwind from camp. It's over there now." The cook pointed his hand to the southwest, where a tarp had been hung between two trees. It was obvious that these guys had hunted from this camp before.

"Make sure you use it," said George, one of the wranglers, "I dug it!"

"This year," continued the cook, "The biggest improvement we have is electricity!"

The cook pointed to the tree where he had installed the electrical outlet. "Now you can clean up after the morning hunt!"

"Do we have to dress for dinner?" It was Ted, one of the hunters. Ted was the organizer of this bunch and kinda in charge.

"Formal dress is not required," answered the cook, unperturbed. "But you will need to be dressed."

The hunters were up early the next morning and out looking for elk. Along towards noon, I brought my hunters into camp, empty handed. We had seen some elk, but didn't get any shots.

Soon after I returned to camp, George arrived with Ted.

"Is lunch ready, Cookie?" Ted always seemed to be hungry.

"Yep," replied the cook.

"I'd like to clean up before I eat," said Ted.

"Everything you need is right over there." The cook pointed to the tree where he had placed the electrical outlet and mirror.

Ted went to his tent and came out carrying his shaving kit. He went to the tree, plugged in his razor without any result.

"This doesn't work!" Ted had his razor plugged in and was switching it on and off. He even slammed it against his open palm a time or two.

"Try the bottom plug," replied the cook.

Ted bent over, unplugged the cord and placed it in the second socket. He turned on the razor without any result.

"This still doesn't work!" Ted was becoming frustrated.

"Maybe it's the altitude," commented the cook.

"No," said Ted. "This is the finest razor money can buy, it's not the altitude." Ted was banging the razor against his hand.

"Is the power on? You know you need power to operate that thing." The cook was showing some genuine concern. "The power switch is on that other tree."

Ted unplugged the cord, went to the other tree and flipped the switch. "That must be it," Ted muttered as he returned to the outlet. He plugged in his razor, without results, switched it on and off a couple of times, then tried the other outlet, without success.

"What's going on here?" Ted was bewildered. "This razor has always worked before."

Ted's problems with his razor had drawn the interest of the other hunters and the guides also. The guides were having a hard time constraining their laughter.

"Maybe it's 'cause there ain't no electricity goin' into the tree," said the cook.

Ted looked for the electric lines above the trees and couldn't find any. Red faced and embarrassed, he got his lunch and was strangely quiet during his meal. He'd been had. But it was all in good fun.

When the hunting season was over, we packed up camp. Everything except the electrical fixtures was removed. No doubt, there was going to be more fun in that camp in the future.

Is Smaller Better?

I got tired of managing my rental horse stable in Grand County, Colorado. Finding good hired help was a problem, and keeping them was another problem. There was a lot of politics involved at the resort where I operated, and the commissions I paid to operate there were certainly cutting into my profit margins. Management had promised to do certain things and they were not making good on their promises. The commission checks I wrote were never late. Also, I spent a lot of money keeping feed in front of the 120 head of horses I had. At times, I felt like I was working for everyone else, including the horses!

And I got tired of dealing with so many tourists. True, they were what made our business, but around the horses most of these people were out of their element. It was a tough job keeping the tourists happy and safe. After a while, it wears hard on a feller, especially when that feller deals with more than a hundred tourists, plus the hired help, every day.

My job duties were pretty much full time, 24 hours a day, 365 days a year. The only time off that I got was to take a day off and go to a horse sale. That was more of a change in routine rather than a day off, but it was a welcome change. And, I've heard a change is just as good as a vacation. I don't know if I agree with that.

After a particularly tough summer with the hired help, and a particularly tough time dealing with the management of the resort where I operated, I got to thinking that a smaller, one-man operation might be a better deal. In fact, a one-man operation began to be real appealing. I would only need to keep myself and the tourists happy, and if I made any money, I could keep it. I wouldn't have any commissions to pay, no payroll to meet; feed for my horses and myself would be my only concern. The way I had it figured, a smaller operation would nearly be heaven.

That fall I didn't renew my contract with the resort. It was a very lucrative contract with a lot of money involved and the potential for a great deal of money was present, but I thought I might be better off dealing with smaller amounts of money that I could keep for myself, with fewer problems and headaches. I sold most of the horses that fall and a lot of the equipment.

The following spring, I set up business at a smaller resort. I had kept ten or twelve horses to operate with. I got a set of portable corrals, found some trails to use, and set up business. The first few days were a little discouraging, but business started to pick up.

I had a cell phone so I could take reservations while I was out on the trail. By keeping a paper and pencil handy, I could set up trail rides while I was out on the trail. The ring tone on the phone was the William Tell Overture, the theme song of *The Lone Ranger* program on radio and television. When it went off out on the trail, it created a little excitement with the trail riders that remembered the program. It was a lot of fun.

In this little bunch of horses I'd kept, there was a little gray horse. I liked to ride Ol' Gray. He'd walk right out, he was plumb gentle, and there wasn't much that bothered him. I liked him mostly because he wasn't very big. He was easy to get on and he handled pretty good. Anybody could ride him, and I rented him out quite a bit.

At this little resort where I was operating, there was also a balloon ride concession. The pilot of this balloon ride deal came over one day to reassure me that his business wouldn't interfere with my horse rides.

"We generally go down the valley, away from where you take your horse rides," he said.

"I certainly hope so," I said. "There's no tellin' what them horses might think if your balloon came down pretty close. It could turn out to be a real rodeo!"

Thoughts of what could happen clouded my mind.

"We'll certainly keep an extra watch out for you," he said as he turned to leave. "We don't want to create any problems."

He may have kept an extra watch out for my trail rides, but he didn't watch close enough.

I had a ride out one morning with just one person. The young lady was probably in her early twenties and indicated that she hadn't rode much before. I figured Ol' Gray would be the perfect horse for her.

We started out through the sagebrush on a two-hour ride. We hadn't been gone half an hour when I noticed a shadow coming across the ground towards us. It was the balloon, and

ONE MILLON HORSE BACK
RIDES - TWO AT A TIME
COME AND SADDLE UP

R. LOREN SCHMIDT.

he was descending right toward us! He was pretty close, and the horse I was riding was starting to act up.

Ol' Gray was just plodding along—he hadn't noticed anything yet. It wasn't very long before Ol' Gray noticed my horse acting up, saw the balloon, and decided he didn't want anything to do with the situation. While he didn't buck, he did a good job of tearing up the ground. The young lady did a good job of controlling him, she didn't fall off, but she was rattled some.

When the balloon landed, I hollered some well-chosen words at the pilot. They weren't the words I wanted to use; I had to choose pretty carefully because the young lady was present.

We continued the ride without incident, and it was a good time. When we got back to the horse barn, the pilot of the balloon was waiting for us. He apologized to me and to the young lady—he apologized profusely. Because the young lady was still present, I couldn't use some better chosen words that I would like to have used!

The summer was a good one. Nobody fell off a horse, and I was able to keep a larger portion of the money I did make.

One day one of my friends, Gary, approached me.

"I want to help you, Stu. I have a horse that needs exercising, and I want to help you and exercise my horse at the same time!"

"Gary," I said, "I don't hardly have enough work here to keep myself busy, much less you, too!"

"That's all right," he replied. "My horse needs the exercise and I don't have anything to do on the weekends." He was quite adamant about helping me, although I didn't need any help.

After a little time explaining my situation, I relented.

"Gary," I said, "You can help me, but there's a few things you need to know. First, there ain't no benefits! There's no insurance, no room an' board, an' no wages. If you make some money in tips, it's yours, but there ain't no guarantees."

Gary agreed, and the following Saturday he showed up with his horse in the stock rack on his pickup. He had a pretty good horse, but he was big, almost too big for his pickup.

I had some rides scheduled for that day, so I had Gary accompany the rides, just to learn the trails. He seemed to do all right; he talked a lot with the tourists. When he was asked a question about his background, he answered it, perhaps with a little too much personal information.

The second weekend, Gary assured me he knew the trails and was ready to take rides out by himself. So, when a couple showed up to go for a ride, I sent Gary as the guide. He did well and brought his riders back safely. I began to send Gary out more frequently. He did a good job.

After a couple of weeks, I asked Gary, "How are you doing in tips? Are you making any money?"

"Not really," replied Gary.

"Tips aren't too good in the rental horse business," I said. "But you should be making some. What are you talking about to your riders?"

"They generally ask me where I'm from, and I tell them."

I knew Gary was from Montana, and I also knew he wanted to go back. He liked Montana better than Colorado.

"Then they ask me, what I'm doing here."

I knew Gary was going through a divorce that he really didn't want.

I interrupted him. "Are you talking about how great Montana is and how rough your divorce is?"

"Well, yes," he replied.

"Don't do that! People don't come from Nebraska or Florida or wherever to Colorado to hear about how great Montana is! And don't talk about how bad your divorce is! And don't talk about how good your horse is! If you want to make a little money in the dude business, show some interest in the dudes!"

"How do you do that?"

"Ask questions of the dudes," I said. "Questions like, 'What do you do for a living?' or 'What brings you to Colorado?' People like to talk about themselves, so ask questions that will tell you something about them. People will be more willing to tip you if you can show a genuine interest in them. Sometimes it's almost like they're paying you to listen to them!"

Gary tried it, and he started to make some tip money. Unfortunately, when he stopped talking about himself to the dudes, he started talking about himself to me! That got old real quick, and I got to thinking that he ought to tip me just for listening to him!

The summer passed without incident. I did have a little profit for my summer's efforts. I did have to turn some riders away because of scheduling, but with Gary present on weekends that didn't happen.

I did refuse a ride to two girls from Japan. I had just come in off a ride. It was raining, and raining hard. I was pretty near soaked clear through. Lightning was striking out in the pasture less than a hundred yards away. The girls wanted to go in the rain, but I refused. I was already wet, and a little more water wouldn't hurt me. But I was afraid of the lightning.

I told the girls to come back the next day, but they didn't show up. I don't think they understood English very well.

The whole summer was fairly easy and quite enjoyable. I think sometimes smaller is better.

Protection

I used to go to a lot of horse sales, mostly to try and buy more horses for my rental horse stable. Occasionally, I'd have something to sell; usually a horse I'd bought that didn't turn out to be what I thought it would be.

Horses that didn't work for me were a liability. I didn't want to keep these misfits because it cost a lot of money to feed them, and if they didn't make any money, I was losing money.

I also looked forward to the horse sales as it was the only break in the routine I had. My rental horse business was a full-time job for me. But going to the horse sales did add an extra burden.

I was usually up around quarter to five in the morning. I'd help get the horses saddled and get the crew lined out for the day. Then, around ten o'clock, I'd hook up the trailer and leave for the sale. Depending on what sale I was going to, I would have a two- or three-hour drive over some pretty high mountain passes before I got to the sale barn.

I would stay at the sale until the last horse was sold, quite often around midnight or one o'clock. The wait generally paid off as the prices tended to get cheaper as the night wore on. By the time I'd get the horses I bought paid for and loaded in the trailer, it would be pretty late. Then I still had the drive home. I would only get a couple hours of sleep before I would have to start the regular routine again. I've been told that a change is as good as a vacation, but on some days I've grown to question that!

At one horse sale, I did get six horses at what I thought was a good price. I was thinking that it wouldn't take long for these horses to start making enough money to pay for themselves, the feed, and then start showing a profit for me. I was feeling pretty smug as I drove home, thinking about how much money I would make.

There is a truck weigh station on the interstate. Vehicles hauling livestock don't generally have to stop, but as there was a particular horse disease making inroads into Colorado, all vehicles hauling livestock were required to stop and show their papers.

I was pretty confident as I crossed the scales. The sign instructed me to come to the office with my papers. I felt that this delay was minor, and I could quickly be on my way. The sale had ended early—it was only around midnight. I was thinking I could get a little more sleep than usual on this horse buying excursion.

I entered the office and showed the gal behind the desk my papers. In Colorado, a bill of sale from an inspected market also serves as a brand inspection. It shows the brands and has a brief description of the animal. An inspected market means that a state brand inspector is present at the sale, and a veterinarian is also present.

"What are you hauling?" The gal behind the desk was pleasant.

"Horses," I replied.

"How many?"

"Six," I said, as I gave her my sale papers.

She smiled as she looked over my papers. Then a frown started to develop on her face.

"Do you have a brand inspection?"

"That's it, lady," I answered.

"No," she said. "This is just a bill of sale. I need a brand inspection."

"That is a brand inspection. In the state of Colorado and most other states, a bill of sale from an inspected market is a brand inspection. I guess it cuts down on the paper work."

The gal didn't believe me. "I need a brand inspection! I'll have to call the brand inspector. Have a seat."

The gal made a phone call. The brand inspector wasn't in, so she left a message. I was getting peeved, worse than that actually. I was perfectly legal, yet being held up. This gal was trying to uphold the law, but she was totally unfamiliar with it. I was starting to get mad. This was uncalled for!

My thoughts turned to the brand inspector. It was Saturday night and he could be anywhere. He might not even show up for a few more hours. I could be stranded here most of the night.

My thoughts then turned to my newly acquired horses. They had been off feed most of the day, and they'd be getting hungry. They could have some colic problems when and if we did get home. And, they were getting restless—the trailer was rocking.

Then, my thoughts turned to myself. I was becoming restless. The extra hour or two of sleep I was looking forward to had vanished. I kept checking my watch. Time was not flying by; it was dragging … very slowly.

The gal noticed my restlessness.

"I'm just trying to protect you," she said.

Protect me, I thought, from who? Me? I don't need protection from myself!

I didn't say anything. This gal was wearing a badge, and I never did think it was a good idea to start an argument with any officer of the law. I was getting madder by the minute, but didn't dare vent my anger. Why make a bad situation worse?

After about an hour, which seemed like two, the phone rang. It was the brand inspector. I didn't hear what was said, but I assume he told the gal the same thing I had: A bill of sale from an inspected market is a brand inspection.

"You're free to go now, Mister Campbell."

I hadn't felt like a prisoner, but it was true. I had been a prisoner, although lacking handcuffs or a cell.

I got my papers and started to leave. I thought about verbalizing my thoughts. I did have some very strong thoughts about not needing protection from myself, thoughts about trying to enforce laws that the law enforcement officials are not familiar with, and thoughts about what a needless waste of time this whole situation had been.

But I thought about it again, and decided to keep my mouth shut. She might not appreciate my thoughts about having incompetent hired help on the payroll. After all, the gal was wearing a badge!

By the time I got to the stables and unloaded the horses, my help had started to show up. My thoughts about grabbing an hour or two of sleep vanished. A new day had begun.

"Do you want to fit saddles to the new horses?" Some of my help was anxious to start.

"No," I replied. "They've had a pretty rough night. We'll give them the day off an' get them ready tomorrow."

"How about you?"

"I ain't in too bad a shape," I said. "I spent the whole night just sittin' around, restin'."

Projecting an Image

It was getting close to the Fourth of July in Jackson, Wyoming. This was supposed to be the cowboy holiday out here in the West, but we had to work.

I was working for Spring Creek Stables, located on one of the buttes overlooking Jackson. The place offered one-, two- and four-hour rides to the general public. It wasn't too bad a job, but after a time, a feller kinda got used to the scenery and started to take it for granted. Then someone would make a remark and a feller might gain a new appreciation of the countryside.

On this Fourth of July, the boss had come up with a new idea. There would be fireworks outside the town of Jackson, and around on the other side of the butte would be an excellent place to watch them. For some extra money, quite a bit of extra money actually, a person could ride horseback up on the butte, watch the fireworks, and then return to the stable for a steak dinner. It was a sure money maker. But it would require some extra work.

We needed some way to secure the horses. The explosions of the fireworks and the sudden lights would surely spook the horses. We couldn't tie them to the buck fence because if they spooked, they could pull the fence down. Then we'd have some, if not all, of our customers walking back to the stables. That wouldn't be acceptable, as it would be a long walk in the dark.

We decided to take up a portable corral. We could use the buck fence as one side of the corral, and string the panels from the portable corral in a big arc back to the buck fence. If we had a couple of hands ride around the outside of the corral, we could kinda sooth the horses if they got spooked during the fireworks.

Carl and I were selected to construct the corral. Carl was a big guy, and the big handlebar moustache he sported made him look even bigger. I thought I had seen him before, making saddles in a saddle shop in Cheyenne, but I couldn't be sure. There are lots of fellers wearing them big handlebar moustaches.

Carl also wore wide suspenders to keep his pants up, and he wore his pants tucked into his boot tops, old-time cowboy style. Also, he always wore a wild rag on his neck, even during the hottest days of summer. He certainly looked the part—an old cowboy right out of a Fredrick Remington or Charlie Russell painting.

I was twenty years older—maybe even more—than Carl. But I never said anything about the way he dressed or the look he was trying to achieve. That was his business, but I couldn't understand his keeping his pants in his boots or wearing a wild rag on the hot days of summer. I surmised that he was trying to prove to everyone, perhaps even himself, that he was a real cowboy.

I never felt that I had to prove to anyone that I was a cowboy. I just accepted the fact as somewhat of a curse, and went about my business.

But I was glad to have Carl help with the corral panels. They were heavy duty and awkward. Carl's muscle was surely appreciated that day.

The afternoon of the Fourth arrived. People started showing up for the fireworks and steak ride about six o'clock. We had some time to visit with the folks before we started to pull horses, bridle them, and tighten cinchas. As I visited with the folks, I thought they were a good group of people and would have a lot of fun. I also thought that this would be a long day.

We got everyone horseback and started out. We arrived at the portable corrals about a half an hour before the fireworks were due to start. I wanted to leave the bridles on the horses and just ear up the reins, but the boss felt that a horse might get the reins caught around the saddle horn on another horse and have a wreck. So we unbridled the horses. This meant we'd just have to put the bridles back on before we could leave. This was going to be a longer day than what I had counted on.

As we got the riders off the horses, we turned the horses loose in the makeshift corral. The riders walked away about a hundred yards to get the best view of the fireworks, and it wasn't long before the fireworks started.

Carl and I had been selected to ride around the outside of the corral and sooth the horses if they became excited. We wouldn't get a view of the fireworks, but that was alright with me. This was all part of the job, and the sooner it was over, the better I would feel about it.

The first blast startled the horses some, but they didn't spook bad. Carl and I were riding around the corral, just talking to the horses to reassure them. For the most part, the horses were just milling around, becoming accustomed to the explosions in the valley below.

I felt sorry for a little sorrel mare we called Peanut. She was at the bottom of the pecking order in that horse herd, and she couldn't find a safe place in the corral. Her running around, trying to find safety, seemed to be causing more problems than the fireworks. Finally, I tied her outside the corral, and the horses settled down some more. The final test would come at the end of the fireworks, when the grand finalé was started. A lot of noise, a lot of lights, and a lot of confusion would follow.

It got a little boring, just riding around the horses, not being able to see much except when the fireworks went off. Carl was riding from the south end of the buck fence and I was coming from the north end. We'd meet in the middle, turn around, ride back to the buck fence, turn around and ride back. It became real boring real fast.

I decided to have a little fun with Carl. At one point, when we met, we stopped to chat some.

"They seem to have settled down good," said Carl.

"Yep," I said. "I don't expect any trouble tonight. They seem to have gotten used to the noise. But, you know, its nights like this when the trouble sneaks up on you. Back in the old days, we used to sing to the cattle to keep them calm."

I was older than Carl, but not so old that I had been on the Texas cattle drives.

"I guess that's how they used to do it," said Carl.

We parted to continue making our quarter-circle rides. When I came to the buck fence and turned around, I could hear Carl singing "The Streets of Laredo." He was actually singing to the horses!

That wasn't really necessary; the portable corral was doing a good job. Then I decided that Carl was trying to convince himself that he was a real cowboy. He was protecting his image, the image he wanted to be.

Knowing that Carl was trying to live up to the image he was trying to project, I didn't say anything on our next pass. But, on the following pass, I decided to have some more fun with Carl.

The next time around, I said, "Carl, that singing is supposed to keep these horses calm. Tone it down some!"

"What's wrong with my singing?"

"I think the horses might appreciate it a lot more if you sang in tune! And tone it down. We don't want you starting a stampede."

Carl didn't say anything; he just turned his horse around to make another pass, and kept singing. He did soften his tone a little.

The fireworks display ended and everyone returned to the stable without incident. It had been a long day.

However, the day did not end without repercussions. Carl was so pleased with his singing to the horses that he started to sing to the dudes on the rides!

Me? I haven't been to a fireworks display since.

Riding Herd

When I got out of the army, I went to Nevada and got a job as a buckaroo. It was early March and it was still quite cold. It was a riding job, but it was kinda boring. We were just riding around the ranch pastures checking cattle every day, and spending the nights in the bunkhouse.

Quite often, when it was really cold and the wind was blowing, we'd split up and go in pairs so we could get the riding done quickly, so we could get in out of the cold. Many times after we split up, we'd get out of sight of the ranch house and the other buckaroos, and drop down into a little swale to build a fire and try to keep warm. I hadn't realized Nevada could be so cold.

Cows were starting to calve, and occasionally we'd have to pull a calf. We'd take the new mother and her calf to a set of corrals and keep them in a day or two so they could get to know each other. We wanted them "mothered up." There wasn't room for any bum calves on this outfit.

Soon, there were enough calves on the ground that we could start branding. There were various sets of corrals scattered around the hay pastures. Some were stack yards—made out of barbed wire or net wire—used to keep the cattle out of the hay, and some were regular pole corrals. They were handy to control the cattle while we branded.

We would rope the calves by both hind legs, drag them to the fire where they would be branded, ear marked, vaccinated, and castrated. To this day, I still get a little disgusted when I see a branding going on when the calves are "headed" rather than "heeled," and dragged up to a fire. Heeling the calves is easier on the animals than catching them by the head. True, it might take a little more skill to catch the calves by the heels than by the head, but I've never met a cowboy or buckaroo who wasn't able to brag some on his roping skills. There weren't any calf chutes on this outfit, no "red ropers." All the cattle had to be roped to be branded or doctored. As far as I was concerned, that is what really made the job fun.

Everybody on the crew had a chance to do some roping. The cow boss was good about giving everyone a turn, although a feller's turn might come only every two or three days. I'm sure everyone had a good time watching my efforts trying to heel some calves. Three years in the army does not help sharpen one's roping skills, and seeing as I wasn't that much good when I went in the army, all I could do was get better. Just like everything else, practice is the key.

When the calves were all branded, the cattle were turned out on the summer range, after they were held for a while so they could mother up. It was important that each calf was with its mother before they were allowed to leave. The ears were counted so we knew how many calves we had branded and the total was entered in the cow boss's tally book.

This outfit had a lot of cattle, and I never did find out exactly how many, but they numbered in the thousands. So there was plenty of work to do.

Soon it was time to go out on the wagon, and we would need some more help. We wouldn't have the benefit of any corrals to brand the calves, so we would need enough hands to hold the cattle while a couple of the hands would rope and a couple of the hands would do the ground work. We also needed a cook and a horse wrangler, or jingle boy.

It would be the jingle boy's job to day-herd the horses and make sure none of them wandered off or snuck back to the home ranch where they wouldn't have to work. I was glad I didn't have that job, it would be pretty boring. There was a fenced pasture close to camp and the horses were turned into it at night, then day-herded during the day outside the pasture to save feed. The jingle boy would have to get up early in the morning and bring the horses in.

The job on the wagon was pretty much routine: up early in the morning, breakfast, saddle up, gather cattle, brand, mother up, then go back to camp. Horses were turned loose and there wasn't much to do until supper.

On the days it rained, we would scatter bulls or pack salt. There was plenty to do even in foul weather. And it was all done from the back of a horse.

Generally, we'd spread out a bedroll and play cards until supper was ready. One day, the jingle boy brought the horses in a little early, turned them into the night pasture and came to the tent to join us in the card game. The cow boss seemed

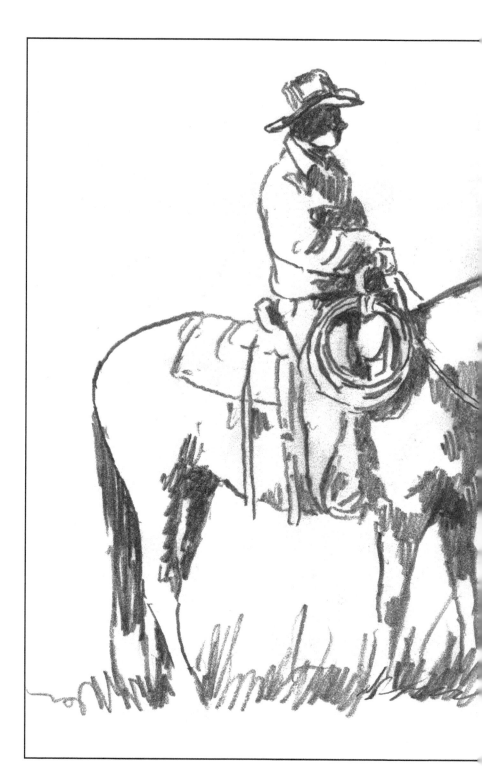

LORE SCHMIDT

a little upset that the horses were brought in early, but didn't say anything.

The jingle boy came into the tent and joined our card game. He took the only available seat—on my bedroll.

Supper was ready and after we ate, we returned to the tent to resume our game. I found a hole, about the size of a quarter, burned in my bed roll tarp. I had just bought that tarp, it was brand new, and that hole was right where the jingle boy had been sitting. I was quite upset and gave the jingle boy a good cussing out about being so careless with his smoking.

As it turned out, the jingle boy quit. The cow boss drove him to the home ranch and left word with the ranch superintendent that we needed a new jingle boy, then returned to the camp.

That night, I was selected to do the jingle boy's job since I had run off the horse wrangler. I didn't like that, but I was up early the next morning and had the horses in before breakfast.

It was a real boring day, keeping watch on the horses. I was getting real restless with not much to do. I knew I might be missing my turn at heeling calves, and nobody knew better than me that I needed the practice. But, even though I felt I had been wrongly accused of running off the jingle boy, and felt justified in my action, I was not a quitter, and felt like I had to do this job to the best of my ability.

I made sure that I kept the horses out longer than the jingle boy had the day before, but I still brought them in a little early—I didn't want anyone thinking that I liked this job.

I hadn't noticed during the day, but we had a visitor. The ranch superintendent had shown up, bringing supplies and a new jingle boy. I was relieved to know that my day herding horses was over. However, even with more practice, my roping didn't improve much.

The cow boss told me later that I hadn't really run off the jingle boy, he had been fixing to leave anyway. My getting upset with him was only his excuse.

A Big Mistake

We had a big ride scheduled at Sombrero Stables in Grand Lake, Colorado. The ride consisted of students from the Air Force Academy in Colorado Springs. About half of the riders were from foreign countries in the Middle East. I would have to split the ride into two sections in order to keep our customer-to-guide ratio in order, and to comply with the national park regulations about the number of horses on the trail at any one time.

I assigned horses and thought I had done a pretty good job. Unbeknownst to me, I had inadvertently assigned all the Middle East students on the same ride and they were to leave in the first section.

I assigned the guides, and because the girl guides on this particular crew were generally slower than the guys in getting people on their horses and adjusting stirrups, I sent the girls out as guides on the first section. We still had fifteen or twenty riders to get mounted, and we had to hurry so that we wouldn't fall too far behind schedule.

R.LOREN SCHMIDT

The first section of the ride left and we went right to work getting the second section ready to leave. It was quite a job, but when they left, I was content that we hadn't got too far behind. It was only an hour ride, and I figured we could make up any time lost during the day. I started to relax some as I resumed my office duties and waited for the first section to return.

Later, I noticed the first section heading in. They were a little late and the second section had almost caught up to them. The guides looked frazzled and tired, and they weren't talking and joking with their riders as they usually did. I went out to help the riders off, and noticed that the girl guides weren't talking to the riders, and the riders weren't following the instructions regarding getting off a horse, Consequently, a few of the riders were hitting the ground with something other than their feet when they got off.

We helped the second section off the horses without incident, then I asked the girls about their ride.

The general consensus seemed to be, "That was a terrible ride!" There were even a few comments about it being "The ride from hell!"

"What happened?" I asked.

The girls started talking all at once. Some of the answers I could comprehend from all their chatter were, "They didn't follow instructions!" "They didn't listen!" "Some of them were trotting and running their horses off the trail!"

I assessed the situation. Apparently I had assigned all the girl guides to a ride in which all the riders were from countries in the Middle East, where women were second-class citizens and the men did not take direction or instruction from the women.

I had made a mistake. I apologized to the girls for not having a broader knowledge of the world situation, and explained to them why they had such a difficult time. I had made a mistake, a big mistake!

Making Money

It was always interesting to watch the new hired help show up for work, particularly the girls. A good deal of time was spent adjusting their hair and applying makeup just right. Shirts and pants were adjusted so they looked as perfect as possible. Certainly these girls were trying to make as good an impression as they could.

I watched with some amusement as the girls showed up for work each morning. They really did look good. I knew that the fancy, cultured look would soon vanish. The good, clean, freshly washed looks didn't last very long. Brushing and saddling close to seventy head of horses each morning doesn't do much for keeping one's good looks looking good. And a cowboy hat isn't too helpful to a fancy hairdo.

Generally, the girls would give up the application of a lot of makeup in favor of a few more minutes of sleep after a few days. Getting ready to work at a rental horse stable doesn't require as much preparation as going to work in an office or going to

TRLOREN SCHMIDT

school. Besides, the horses don't really care what the hired help looks like. They just want their feed in the morning!

Of course, working around horses is dirty. Hay and grain dust get all over a person and the oil used on the saddles rubs off on clothing, generally bringing with it the accumulation of the dust from the trail. Clean clothes were nice, but they didn't really stay clean long. Consequently, the good looks of the girls took on a ranch look. They still looked good, but they didn't give the impression they were going out to an office job, or going out to catch a man.

Marcy was a gal from the south that we hired in the spring of 2008. She had been a cocktail waitress, but she had a horse background and she wanted to get back to horse related work. She was only about twenty-one or so, and she had learned how to apply makeup. She had learned well!

After a few weeks, Marcy had decided to go to town on her day off. She left unnoticed and no one gave her a second thought as we were busy conducting the day's business, taking tourists out on guided horseback rides.

We were seated at the supper table when Marcy returned. She was dressed to the hilt with a low-cut blouse, a mini skirt that was shorter than it needed to be, and more makeup than she really needed! She did look sharp!

Everyone stopped eating as she made her entry into the dining room. I was speechless, and conversations stopped as she entered. She certainly commanded everyone's attention. We really weren't used to seeing our co-workers dressed in anything but their work clothes.

Someone asked, "How was your day off?"

Jason got right to the point when he hollered, "Did you make any money?"

Marcy had got herself all fixed up—fixed up to the point where she looked just like a hooker!

A Day Off

It's real handy to get a day off, and I do take a day off every time I get a chance. I have too much to do to not take a day and take care of my own business. Unlike the hired help, I can't sleep in on a day off.

In addition to doing laundry, getting a haircut, and taking care of my housekeeping duties, I also have a hundred mile round trip just to get the mail once a week. What comes in the mail dictates what else I have to do on my day off. Consequently, a lot of my free time isn't free.

I never could understand the hired help. Invariably, they would sleep in on their day off, eventually get up, and then come to the horse corrals, saddle a horse and go for a ride. True, the scenery is fantastic in Rocky Mountain National Park, but it's the hired help's job to lead guided horseback rides through the park. I always got enough of the scenery on the job. It seemed kinda strange to me that the help would want to go for a ride on their day off.

It's Going to Be A Long Day!
BY R LOREN SCHMIDT

In addition to running the office, making change, assigning horses, and guiding rides, part of my duties as barn boss is to clean the corrals. Fortunately, we have a bobcat with a bucket to do this. It generally takes a couple of hours to clean the night corral and an hour or so to clean the day pen. I don't look forward to doing this because it's a dirty job. The manure dust can get on the bobcat pretty easy, and I generally come out of the bobcat covered in dust. I try to plan on doing this the day before my day off. It makes doing laundry worthwhile. There's no sense in washing clean clothes!

On one particular day, two of the girls wanted to go for an extended ride on their day off. I listened as they asked Dave for permission to go.

"How long will you be gone?"

Dave had been put in the position where he had to go out after business hours to look for lost hired help.

"Only about five hours," replied one of the girls.

"Well, you girls can go, but make sure you're back on time. I don't want to be out all night looking for you!"

The girls thanked him and left.

"I can't understand why the hired help all want to go for a horseback ride on their day off," I said. "Don't they get enough riding during the work week?"

"I guess not," replied Dave. "When and where do you want to go riding on your next day off?" Dave was joking with me some as he asked the question.

"Well, I replied, "I been meanin' to ask you. With all the rain we've had the last couple of weeks, an' the way the manure has built up in the corral, an' as long as it's taken me to clean it all up, do you think I could take the bobcat out for a spin on my day off?"

Dave just grinned. "Use your own judgment," he replied.

I did not take the bobcat out for a drive on my next day off!

Splitting Tips

When we hire new help at our rental horse stables, we're never really sure what we've got until the new hand shows up. We generally hire college students for the summer—it makes a good summer job and it can be fairly profitable for them if they bank their wages and live off their tips.

The problem for us once we've hired a good crew comes in August when a lot of the help has to return to school. Then we're short-handed, but we do have the opportunity to have job applicants saddle, bridle, and ride a horse in order to evaluate their skills.

We did hire a young feller that didn't have much work or horse experience one year. I wondered if this guy had ever had a job away from home before. The cook wondered if he had ever been out of the house before! Sometimes we hire some really immature help. I had it figured that Mike was in that category.

Mike showed up early in June, sometime after we had completed our intensive training sessions. I conduct the training and it becomes kinda repetitive for me and the help. I did do some training one-on-one with Mike, but he had to learn a lot while on the job.

We have a customer-to-guide ratio at the stables of eight customers to one guide. We try to keep the rides as small as possible, but often have to send out an extra guide for safety purposes. Mike, because of his inexperience in riding horses and apparent lack of maturity, became the second guide on many trail rides. Often, I had to caution the other guides that they had another tourist to watch when I sent Mike on a ride with them. This didn't sit well with a lot of the other help.

The guides are expected to split any tips they get with the other guides on the ride. Some of the other guides didn't like having Mike on the rides as he didn't do much, and what he did do had to be double-checked. When he did enter into conservation with the tourists, which was quite often, it was generally about computer games and more technical stuff, rather than horses or about Rocky Mountain National Park. The other guides thought Mike detracted from their ability to make tips.

I was on a ride with Mike when the wind suddenly came up, the grass started blowing, the horses spooked and one guy fell off. Even though Mike was only one horse behind the guy that fell off, and I was on the tail end of a seventeen-person ride—about eight horses behind Mike—I got to the scene of the incident before Mike. The guy was not injured and completed the ride, but I did have to talk to Mike about watching his riders.

Mike's inexperience became even more apparent when he was asked about what the horses were doing.

One customer thought his horse was trying to bite him and when he asked, "What is my horse doing? I think he's trying to bite me," Mike's reply was "I don't know."

The horse was simply trying to get the flies off his belly.

Another customer nicknamed Mike "Lightning Rod." The customer had convinced Mike that he should stand up in the stirrups when they got caught in a thunderstorm. Mike thought it was funny when he came into the stables in that position. I thought it was kinda, no, outright dumb.

We did keep Mike on for the summer, although I wondered why. I did have him doing a lot minor jobs, and thought he might do better as a chore boy rather than a guide.

I sent Mike out as a second guide with Pat one day. Pat was prone to getting a little discouraged when he didn't get a tip on a ride. I was surprised to see Pat in good spirits after the ride, even though he and Mike didn't get a tip.

"What's happening?" I was curious.

"We didn't make a tip on that ride," said Mike.

Mike was always ready to give an answer or opinion, even though the question wasn't directed at him.

"No, we didn't get a tip," answered Pat. "But it's alright. Mike has agreed to split this week's allowance with me!"

Pat's reply was an obvious humorous reference to Mike's immaturity and the fact that he hadn't been away from home before. Mike was oblivious to the comment or situation.

Picking up on the reference to his immaturity, I asked, "So, what are you going to do with a quarter?"

"I don't know," replied Pat. "I'll certainly have to watch my finances!"

I did have some fun with Mike's family when they came up to ride. Generally we give a discount to members of the hired help's family.

When Mike's family showed up, I was running the office.

"So you're Mike's mom," I said. I had talked to her many times on the phone as she called frequently to see how her son was doing. This had further confirmed the cook's suspicions that this was his first time out of the house. I had come to believe the cook was right!

"Yes. We have a reservation to ride with Michael," came the reply.

I had a lot of reservations about Mike on a ride, but didn't say anything. After all, if someone did fall off on this ride, Mike's parents wouldn't sue us if Mike was incompetent.

"We usually give a discount to family members when they ride," I said. "But we haven't got the work out of Mike that we expected, so I've been authorized by my boss to charge you folks double!"

Mike's mom looked a little surprised and started to object, but I cut her off.

"I'm only jokin', lady." I added quickly. "Actually, we're goin' to let you go for half price!"

Mike's mom looked relieved, but I'm sure, from the look on her face and her reaction to my funning, that she knew exactly what we were dealing with!

After Mike's ride with his family, I heard Pat ask him, "Did you make a tip on that ride?"

"No."

"Well," asked Pat, "did you get your allowance?"

I didn't hear the answer.

Scar

"What's your horse's name, Grandpa?"

It was Jade, my nine-year-old granddaughter. Her mom was riding Leopard. I was surprised Jade had remembered Leopard's name—it had been a year since they had come up to go riding. It was kinda obvious; Leopard was the only leopard Appaloosa horse we had in the rental horse string. Jade was riding Sarge, her favorite horse from the year before.

Sarge was a real good horse for anybody, especially kids or small women. He just marched the trail, never causing any problems, and didn't even try to graze. Everyone that rode Sarge loved him.

"Well, Sis, I call him Scar."

"How come?"

"See that big gouge in his neck? That's a scar that kinda sets him apart." I turned the horse on the trail so Jade could get a better look.

"How did he get it?"

Actually, I don't know how he got the scar; he had it when we bought him. From the location and the angle, I speculated that it had been from some sort of roping accident. It had been fairly deep and somebody had taken the time to sew it up and doctor it. The scar was still deep even though it had healed completely. It was just unsightly, but it didn't bother him or his performance.

I didn't want to appear totally ignorant in front of my granddaughter, so I said to her, "I did it!"

"Why did you do that to your horse, Grandpa?"

"It was a matter of life or death, darling."

"Life or death?"

"Yep. That horse saved my life."

"How did he save your life, Grandpa?"

"Well," I said, "we were out riding the mountain, looking for stray cows, when all of the sudden, a blizzard hit … "

"Where did it hit, Grandpa?" Jade was not shy about interrupting to ask a question.

"It hit me right in the chest, Sis. Knocked me plum off my horse. When I hit the ground, my head hit a rock an' knocked me out. I woke up three days later under four feet of snow. It was all white an' warm. I thought I'd died an' went to heaven."

"How can it be warm under cold snow?"

"I don't know," I answered. "But I had to dig out from under three feet of snow and …"

"Four feet of snow," interrupted Jade, "and three days."

"Yeah. I was kinda groggy. But I still had Scar. I'd held onto the reins the whole time."

"What are the reins, Grandpa?"

"Reins are them leather things you got in your hand. I was unconscious an' had held onto Scar for four days."

"Three days," corrected Jade, "and four feet of snow."

"That's right," I continued. "I was real hungry; I hadn't ate for four days and …"

"Three days and four feet …"

"I know, I know." I was becoming a little perturbed with Jade constantly interrupting and correcting me. But at least she was listening.

"I was really hungry," I continued, "An' Scar was just standing there, an' pert near froze to the ground. So, I brushed the snow off him, there was three feet of snow on him, and …"

"Four feet …"

"No. Three feet of snow. Some of it had melted!" I'd be darned if I was going to let this nine year old get the best of me. "An' I brushed the snow off him, took out my pocket knife an' sliced off a slab of his neck. Then he became unfroze an' jerked away, or I'd have got more."

"How did he become unfroze?"

"He thawed out; that is he woke up." I was going to have to watch my wording a little closer. I certainly didn't want to get into a linguistic debate with this youngster—numbers were bad enough.

"I got some dry firewood an' started a fire to cook up my steak and …"

"Where did you get dry firewood under four feet of snow?"

"It was under me, I …"

"But you landed on a rock, Grandpa."

"Only my head, dear, only my head," I answered. "The rest of my body kept the snow off the firewood an' kept it dry.

"Well, I got the fire lit an' cooked up my fillet …"

"What's a fillet Grandpa?"

"A fillet is like a steak without a bone. But I cooked up my steak an' ate it right on the spot. Good thing, too, 'cause I was gettin' awful weak …"

"This story is going to take a week," muttered Jade.

Jade's Mom let out a big laugh. "You might be right, Jade!"

"… after not eating for four days," I continued.

"Three days!"

"Yep, three days. After I got done eatin', I pulled some hair from Scar's tail so I could sew up his wound. It was cold enough that the bleedin' had stopped."

"How cold was it, Grandpa?"

"It must have been twenty or thirty below," I answered.

"Below? What was it under?"

"What do you mean under?" I was starting to become confused.

"If it was below something, then it had to be under something," answered Jade. "Under what?"

"The thermometer," I answered. This was becoming a rather difficult story.

"I brushed five feet of snow off my saddle, an'…"

"Four feet," corrected Jade.

"No! Five feet! Some more snow had blown onto my saddle while I was cookin' my supper. But I got back in the saddle an' rode back to the ranch. An' that's how Scar got his name."

"Are you sure, Grandpa?"

"Yep!"

"What did you do during the three days you were knocked out?"

"I just laid out there on the desert an' …"

"Mountain."

"Yep, I just laid out there on the mountain an' froze."

"You didn't freeze, Grandpa!"

"I sure did! An' I can prove it!"

"How?"

"See these gray hairs on my head? They haven't thawed out yet. That's why they're gray."

"Grandpa, I'm not so sure I can believe you!"

"Well, darling, I certainly wouldn't intentionally mislead you, would I?"

"I don't know," answered Jade. "But why didn't you just name him Daisy or something?"

"Daisy wouldn't be a good name for a gelding and Something ain't even a name. Scar is about the only tag that would fit him. But he earned the name, savin' my life!"

"You could have called him 'Lifesaver' or something else."

"Lifesaver wouldn't fit him. A lifesaver has a hole in it," I answered.

"Just like your story and your head!" Jade's reply was matter-of-fact.

Jade's mom laughed in agreement, and I wondered why I didn't just name him Daisy or something!

Looks Ain't Everything

Jake came to work for us in the spring of 2010. He was young, only about nineteen. He hadn't worked around horses much, but was willing to learn. He didn't dress much like a cowboy or horseman, but we changed that pretty quickly. He reverted to his prior ways on his day off and dressed sorta weird on his own time.

Jake did have the capacity to learn, and seemed anxious to learn everything he could about the horses. It wasn't long before he was guiding our tourist horseback rides on his own. However, his desire to learn everything hampered his ability to adequately perform the job he was doing.

He also had the capacity to say the wrong thing at the wrong time. Sometimes he said the right thing at the right time and it still came out wrong!

He arrived without a car or truck and I wondered if he knew how to drive. He pestered me quite often about driving the feed truck, so one day I relented.

We had just finished feeding in the early evening, and were closing the gate into the night pen.

"Can I drive the feed truck?"

"Can you drive a four-speed, a manual tranny?"

"Sure," answered Jake.

"I guess," I answered. "Take it over an' put it in front of the hay barn."

Jake eagerly got into the cab and started the truck—but he couldn't get it to move.

"Put it in gear," I hollered.

"It is," was Jake's reply.

"Well, it ain't movin'," I muttered. "Put it in the right gear, granny gear or first gear!"

Jake fiddled around in the cab, revved up the engine without getting the truck to move.

Fearing a mechanical breakdown on the only feed truck we had, I started toward the truck. After all, we had to keep almost 90 head of horses fed every morning and night.

"Better let me take it over," I said, as I climbed in the truck.

I put the truck in gear, let off the parking brake, and drove the truck to the hay barn.

"These things generally move better with the brake off," I said.

"Well … yeah," said Jake. "The knob on the gearshift confused me. I thought you did things different down here."

Jake was from Canada and the knob was on kinda tilted. It had a habit of slipping off and would be put back on in any manner that happened to be handy.

"We don't do things that different," I said.

On another occasion, I had just loaded a bale of hay on the truck with the bobcat. We use big 1,100-pound bales and the bobcat is mighty handy getting the hay bales on the truck. There is a slope in front of the hay barn where the truck was loaded and Jake wanted to know if he could move the truck.

"Sure," I said. "Don't forget to take off the brake!"

Jake got in the truck, started it, popped the clutch and peeled out. By the time he stopped, the dust had cleared and the bale had slid halfway off the bed of the truck!

I had put the bobcat away, but had to get it out again to push the bale back on the truck bed.

"I think your days of drivin' the feed truck have come to an end," I said.

"When can I drive the bobcat?"

The bobcat was another matter. It was all we had to load hay with, and the only way to clean the corrals. Jake would not be driving the bobcat! Driving the bobcat was something that required some thought about what you were doing while you were doing it. I wasn't sure Jake was capable of doing that.

It would have been nice to have someone to run the bobcat when we had to clean the corrals. That was a dirty dusty job and as barn boss, it was mine. I didn't really look forward to it. The corrals weren't really level, there were a lot of rocks, and it was difficult to do a good job. In addition, someone had removed the bobcat door, so every time the bucket was dumped, a lot of the corral dust would end up in the cab.

I was cleaning the corral one day and had Jake watching the gate for me so the saddled horses wouldn't get in with the unsaddled ones. The conditions were pretty good; the corral was

R. Loren Schmidt

still a little damp from a rainstorm the day before, and there wasn't much dust.

I thought I'd done a pretty good job and was a little proud of how it looked. As I drove out the gate, I stopped to see what Jake thought of it.

"How does it look?" I was halfway fishing for a compliment.

"It looks pretty good," said Jake, "but it still looks like horse crap!"

It was also difficult to get a compliment from Jake.

Missing Horses

In the fall I used to rent out horses for hunters. I stopped doing it for a number of reasons, all of them valid.

One hunter had lost his horse. It took three days of riding to try and find the horse, but we never did. We left word with all the other hunters we ran into about what we were looking for, and left a business card with a phone number on it. We also left a description of the horse with the brand, STU, on the left shoulder.

Another hunter had found the horse, tied him to a tree, and gave us a call. My oldest son, Will, got the call and went and retrieved the horse. He was missing his saddle and bridle, but still had his halter.

I had cashed the guy's deposit check, and had to refund it, less the replacement cost of the saddle. For all the time spent hauling our saddle horses, riding unfamiliar country looking for the lost horse—it was not a real profitable situation.

A lady found the saddle the following spring, and I got a call from the sheriff of that county informing me that my lost saddle had been found. I had to tell the sheriff that I had charged the hunter for the saddle and as far as I was concerned, it was his.

Actually, I had charged the hunter for more than the saddle was worth, and didn't want to buy back a saddle that had laid out on the ground all winter, exposed to the elements.

⊗

I went to pick up another horse I'd rented out for a hunt. As I loaded the horse, Booger, the hunter commented, "That horse sure can buck!"

Buck? I'd never known Booger to buck, and I had owned him for seven or eight years.

Carefully, I ran my hand over his back. He had a swelling over his kidneys, and as I ran my hand over the area, he almost dropped to his knees.

"Here! Look at this!" I was quite upset.

The hunter stepped up into the truck. I ran my hand over Booger's kidney area again. Not only did he almost drop to his knees, he tried to kick me.

"I've never seen this horse buck! You've given him a serious kidney sore! It'll take all winter for this to heal, if it heals at all."

The hunter had jumped back when the horse kicked, and I didn't know if the look of surprise, shock, and fear was because of the horse's actions or my tone of voice.

"Any horse will buck to avoid the pain or injury of puttin' up with a condition like this."

I was really getting mad, and was ready to inflict some pain on this hunter equal to what Booger was enduring. But I remembered that this guy was a hunter with a gun, and it was probably loaded!

I checked the saddle blankets and pads. They were covered with mud, leaves, sticks, and about half frozen with ice. This conglomeration of debris would be enough to sore anything.

◌∞◌

Another party had lost all four horses they had rented. I got the call late one night, and the next day I got a saddle horse and went to look for my lost horses. I rode to their camp, and nobody was there. I hoped they were hunting horses rather than elk.

The hunters had fashioned a make-shift corral by nailing some aspen tree limbs to trees that were handy. It wasn't a strong corral, and I could see where the limbs had been broken and the horses escaped.

I trailed the horses as far as I could, but had to stop because daylight had run out. I headed back to the hunter's camp. They had returned from their hunt.

When I asked them what happened, they said they didn't know. According to them, something had spooked the horses during the night and they had run off. I told them to keep looking for the horses and that I'd be back the next day.

I didn't get an early start the next day. I deposited their deposit check in the bank on the way to look for the horses. I also took another guy to help in the hunt.

When we unloaded our saddle horses at the trailhead, I checked out the hunters' vehicle. It was a station wagon type vehicle, and still loaded with baled hay. It looked like they had packed their gear to camp and forgot to come back for the horse feed. When we arrived at the camp, I carefully checked the corral they had built—there wasn't a straw of hay on the ground. The horses very easily could have broken the aspen limbs reaching for grass outside the corral.

Our hunt was unsuccessful. We rode that country for five days and couldn't find the horses. I was perplexed. Normally when a horse gets loose in new country, he'll return to the spot where he was unloaded from the trailer, but these horses were nowhere to be found.

During our hunt for the horses, the hunters' deposit check was returned, marked "insufficient funds." I immediately hired a lawyer. I was out four horses, a bum check, and the replacement cost of the horses.

As it turned out, I did recover one of the horses, but had to take the hunters to court to recover the replacement costs. I didn't find any humor in the situation and decided not to rent out hunting horses in the future. The money wasn't always good!

"Details"

I had known Jack for some time. We had a lot in common, both of us being old cowboys. Jack was a little older than me, and quite often our "bull" sessions over a cup or two of coffee became "can you top this?" sessions. I would bet that there were more wild horses caught and more broncs rode during these sessions than were ever caught or rode in our lifetimes by either one of us.

I'm not so sure that I believed everything Jack told me, although he had no reason to embellish the truth, but I enjoyed listening to his stories. I know I didn't believe everything I told him, but I think he believed part of it.

After a lot of stories by both of us and many sessions, Jack began repeating himself. Some of his previously told tales sounded a little different the second time than they did during their first telling.

I called him on this once when he started to tell of an experience I'd already heard about.

R Loren Schmidt

"Are you starting to repeat yourself, Jack? I think I remember hearing this before, only a little different. I think you might be embellishing your stories some!"

That was as nice as I could say that Jack was lying to me without coming right out and calling him a liar.

Jack gave me a funny look, almost like he thought I disbelieved him.

"No. No, I ain't changin' my story none, I'm just adding detail!"

"I guess that's all right, I generally don't pay much attention to detail," I answered.

Jack continued his story, adding more "detail" as he proceeded. His story became quite involved.

I continued to tell my stories, also adding "detail" as I deemed necessary. These bull sessions were becoming a little tiresome and each one of us was running out of "detail" to make our stories better than the other's.

One day we decided to go to the horse races. It was early spring and the races were just starting. I hadn't had much interest in the local horse races, although I did have some interest in the Triple Crown and the Breeder's Cup.

"Ever do much bettin' on the races?" Jack asked.

I thought Jack was trying to set me up to win some money off me, but I answered him truthfully.

"No," I said. "I didn't know bettin' was legal in Utah."

"It's legal all right. They made it legal a couple of years ago. They even got bettin' windows, just like the Kentucky Derby!"

This was all new to me, and finding out that Jack wasn't trying to get some of my money for himself, I started to relax some.

"I'll show you how it works."

We went to the betting windows, got a couple of programs, and settled down in the stands as the horses were led out on the track.

"Now you pick the one you think will win, look at the odds, place your two-dollar bet, an' hope he wins," said Jack.

That sounded simple enough, so I picked a horse, placed a bet, and watched as my horse finished last.

"How did your horse do? All the time you've spent around horses, you should have picked a winner," said Jack.

"He didn't do so good," I answered. "He finished last. But as far as he was behind the rest of them horses, he stands a good chance of winnin' the next race!"

"Pick you a better one on the next race!"

I picked another horse, paid my money, and sat down to watch my pick come in last again.

"Didn't you pick a winner?" Jack was leaving to go to the pay window.

"Nope. My horse came in dead last again. In fact, he was so far behind, he must have thought he was leadin'."

We spent the whole day at the race track, and I couldn't pick a winner all day. I was pretty discouraged.

"I can't pick a winner," I mumbled, more to vent my frustration than to seek advice. But Jack heard me.

"Want me to tell you what you're doin' wrong?"

I didn't really want him to. I wasn't so sure he wouldn't furnish more "detail" than I needed. But, I consented.

"First of all, you're pickin' horses that you would pick to ride on a big circle, not horses that can run fast for any distance."

"But I'm pickin' good horses," I said. "I sure wouldn't have picked that sway-backed nag you picked in that one race."

"Yep," said Jack, "they're good horses, but not the best for this. They got to be able to run. If they had any cow sense, they'd be out on a cow ranch, or entered in a ropin,' or cutting, or reinin' show somewheres. You got too much old cowboy in you to be a race horse man. Besides that, the old sway-backed nag, as you called him, won!"

"But I do know somethin' about a horse!" I was becoming a little agitated in addition to being discouraged.

"Second," Jack continued, ignoring my protestations, "you're pickin' horses to win. You ought to be pickin' 'em to win, place, or show."

"What does that mean?" I guess I was a little green at this horse racing business.

"First, second, or third, they pay to three places."

"I didn't know that," I said. "You didn't tell me! I got incomplete information."

"Next, you should pick the horses you think will win, and then bet on the others. That way you might win some.

"Fourth, next time you come to the races, bring your lunch an' leave your money home. You won't win anything, but you won't lose anything, either."

I didn't really have anything to say. I think the old man told me as nice as he could that I wasn't any good at picking horses. I think he told me straight, without adding any "detail."

Old Friends

I went to work for Sombrero Stables in June of 1986. I had got the job through Steve's mother, Sue.

Steve had me running a little satellite stable up at Grand Lake Lodge, outside of Grand Lake, Colorado. There were only ten rental horses there and Steve used the location to hide out some lame horses and to keep access to Rocky Mountain National Park open through the Grand Lake Lodge property. I don't think he really expected to make much money on the deal, but they had done it for years. It appeared to be a necessary business expense.

However, I started selling some horseback rides and was bringing home some money each night. I did enough business that Steve gave me some good horses I could use, rather than the lame or sore-backed horses he wanted to hide out.

We made a pretty fair go of the deal for the first two summers, then Steve was called away on some personal business, and I was left to manage the main stable in Grand Lake.

The following summer I opened my own stable operation between Granby and Winter Park, Colorado. I didn't see much of Steve for a few years, although he did come by my stables to shoe horses for a few days.

Steve's dad, Pat, died and I owed Pat some money. I saw Steve at the funeral; Steve had moved to Iowa. A year or so later, I had some extra money and made arrangements to go to Iowa and pay off the remainder of what I owed to Pat to Steve.

I ended up selling my stable and going into semi-retirement some years later. I still had to work and spent four or five years guiding trail rides in the Jackson Hole area in Wyoming, and a couple of years in the Durango, Colorado, area. I ended up outside Estes Park, Colorado, guiding horseback rides in the eastern part of Rocky Mountain National Park.

Steve had moved from Iowa to the Wheatland, Wyoming, area. Some years previously, I had seen a flyer advertising BLM horses and Steve Mantle. I called the number on the flyer figuring on meeting up with Steve and visiting for a while. If anybody could handle those wild horses, I figured Steve could do it.

I called the number on the flyer and was met with a cordial, "Hello." It was Steve's wife, Christy.

I thought I would have a little fun and act like a greenhorn.

"Yes." I said. "I saw a flyer for BLM horses in a saddle shop and would like a little more information. Is this BLM horse a new breed or something? I don't think I've ever heard of them before. What can you tell me about them?"

"You'll have to talk to my husband," was Christy's reply. "I'll get him for you."

Christy turned away from the phone. I could hear her as she said, "Steve, this call's for you. Somebody wants to know about BLM horses. It sounds like Stu Campbell!"

I hadn't talked to Christy for some years and didn't realize my voice would be so easily identifiable. I decided to try and keep up my ruse.

"Hello."

I recognized Steve's voice.

"Yes sir," I said, "I saw your flyer about BLM horses and wanted to know what you can tell me about this new breed of horse. I don't think I ever heard of them before. What are …?"

I was interrupted.

"Howdy, Old Timer! How you been?" Steve was the only one that called me "Old Timer" at such a young age.

I had been recognized.

We visited on the phone for a while and Steve told me that he had a deal with the Bureau of Land Management to take some of the older wild horses that had been gathered off BLM land, gentle them down, start them under a saddle, then offer them up for adoption under their Wild Horse and Burro Adoption Program. It sounded like a pretty good deal as long as a guy could stay healthy doing it. I didn't get all the particulars on it, but it appeared that Steve was doing alright with the deal.

I didn't get a chance to see Steve in person as he and I both had other commitments, but it was good to visit with him on the phone.

A few years later I saw a flyer in a saddle shop in Laramie, Wyoming, where Steve was conducting a seminar over two days on how to handle these wild horses.

R. LOREN SCHMIDT

I got a day off the next week and went to Laramie just to visit with Steve. I hadn't signed up for his clinic, I figured I'd just go and visit with him when he had a free minute or two. When I got to Laramie, Steve was just finishing up his clinic.

"Hey, Old Timer! How you doing?" Greetings from Steve were always cordial.

"How you doin'? How's your horse clinic?" I had a lot of questions, as I hadn't seen Steve for quite a few years.

We visited for a long time, questioning each other on where we had been and what we had been doing. Finally I asked him, "How often do you do these seminars or horse clinics?"

"We do quite a few of them," replied Steve. "We've done them all over Wyoming, Montana, and Colorado. And we're doing okay with them."

"Ever see any of the kids that worked for us in your travels?"

Steve directed his kids in what to do before he answered. I was surprised at how his kids had grown over the years. The last time I had seen them, they were only three or four years old. Now they were young adults in their early twenties.

I remembered that first summer I worked for Steve. I had worked all the way into August without taking a day off. I finally took a day, and went to town and got some new shirts and a haircut. That night at supper, with my new haircut, one of Steve's kids kept looking at me.

Finally he asked, "Is that Stu?"

My reminiscing was interrupted.

"Occasionally, I see some of the people that worked for us," Steve brought me back to the present. "Of course, there were so many that I've forgotten a lot of them.

"On the other hand, I've done a few clinics down at the state and federal prisons outside Florence, Colorado. The prison system has a program where the inmates can sign up to green break these wild horses and take the edge off them as part of their rehab program. It seems to work pretty well for them. There were only four or five guys signed up for the clinic, but I knew all of them. They had all worked for Dad at some time or another.

"You never know where or when you'll run into some of your old friends!"

Still Embarrassed

I was the foreman on a dude ranch when I was going to college. My wife was the cook. It was a good job for the summer—the money was good and the work easy and pleasant.

The ranch only owned one horse, an old mare, a pensioner they called Peanut. The horse was so old, she was often considered for use as bear bait. We did use her occasionally as a small kid's horse, but not very often. The ranch leased all the other horses from an outfitter, but they only needed ten or twelve.

The ranch was located in Grand Teton National Park, in Wyoming. In the early days, it had been a real going concern and I've heard they had close to a hundred head of horses. The original owner had passed away before I hired on, and the place was being operated during the summer by his wife. The place was beginning to show signs of disrepair, but the guests didn't seem to mind. They had an opportunity to rough it to some degree.

The horses were delivered a week or so before the first guests showed up. Wanting to impress the owner with my knowledge and skill, I felt like I should "top off," or ride, each one before I put the guests on them. I also needed to do this so I knew what I had. Unbeknownst to me, all the horses had been at the ranch the summer before and the owner knew them better than I did. But, I still needed to get acquainted with them.

The only hired help I had was the owner's grandson, and we set out to riding our string of horses. There wasn't much excitement during this process and I was a little disappointed, but also somewhat relieved. Having a bunch of bucking horses or broncs on a dude outfit is not a good idea, unless there is a wrangler around that can ride them.

We were fortunate that we could turn the horses out every night and not have to feed them. I did keep them in for a few days and grained them every day so they would stay close to home. There were not any fenced pastures on this ranch, and if they wanted to, they could go anywhere they wanted.

In this bunch of horses was a good looking paint they called Salty. I picked him for a guide horse because he neck-reined and would spin a little. I do like a horse that will do what he's been asked or told to do without an argument. Too often, dude horses are so used to doing the same thing every day, a feller can't get them to do anything else without a good tune-up.

There was also a big blue roan horse that I kept in fairly often to use as a jingle horse to gather the others in the morning. I think this horse was called Badger, or something like that. There was also a black mare with some white markings, and the rest were sorrels and bays. All in all, it was a pretty good string of dude horses.

I got to feeling a little sorry for Badger. All the other horses got a chance to get out at night and get a good feed, but Badger didn't get that opportunity very often. I began keeping another horse in at night and giving Badger an opportunity to get some fresh feed.

I selected the horses to keep in at random, preferring to ride some of them more than others. Quite by chance, I decided to keep the black mare in one night. It was towards the end of the summer, and I hadn't rode the mare since she first arrived. I was kind of an old cowboy, even in my younger days, and have always preferred to ride geldings.

I went to bed that night not expecting any trouble or difficulty the next morning. The horses were always easy to find, and were generally close to the corrals looking for their grain. The grain was their reward, a little in the morning and a little at night.

The next morning, I saddled the black mare and headed out to look for my horses. The ranch was located along the Snake River below a big sagebrush flat. It was easy to ride up on the flat and look for the horses in the willows along the river.

But this morning, the horses were nowhere to be found. I assured myself that the horses weren't along the river and started searching the flat. I couldn't see any horses on the flat I was on and went up on the second bench.

On the second bench, I could see a dark object moving west.

That's got to be Badger, I thought, and started the mare into a trot to head him home. But I couldn't see any other horses. I thought that was strange, but I was confident that when I found Badger, I would find the other horses close by.

As I got closer to the object, I could see it wasn't Badger. It was a moose!

It struck me as funny to see a moose in the middle of a sagebrush flat. They're generally seen around water or areas where there's a lot of willows, and this moose was about six miles from the river.

My horses weren't with the moose and the moose wasn't with the horses. I didn't know where they were. They had vanished!

I went back to the bench where I could see the river again. Carefully, I looked over the whole area without seeing a horse. I didn't know where they were. I had been out looking for my horses for about two hours without success, and I was convinced they had left for good. I returned to the ranch for breakfast, not knowing what to do.

"Did you find your horses this morning?" It was the boss lady. The way she asked the question, made me believe she knew something I didn't.

"Nope," I replied. "I don't know where they are."

"I do," answered the owner.

"How do you know? Where are they? Have they done this before?" I had plenty of questions and was totally perplexed.

"They have done this occasionally in the past. They're up at Jenny Lake."

I was beginning to think that my horses were playing some sort of childish prank on me.

"How do you know they're there?"

"The outfitter called me and told me our horses had come home."

I didn't waste any time in getting my saddle into the truck. The boss lady volunteered to drive me to Jenny Lake. I could saddle one horse and trail my stray's home.

When we arrived at Jenny Lake, my stray horses were in a corral. I could swear they were grinning, enjoying the prank they

R LOREN SCHMIDT

had pulled. To me, they looked like they were trying hard to conceal their merriment!

"What are you doing with my horses?"

The outfitter was there to greet us, with a big smile on his face.

"They were here when I got up," he replied. "I don't know how long they've been here."

"How come they're here? I rode plenty this mornin' lookin' for 'em," I said.

"To me, that's pretty simple," answered the old timer. "They're all geldings an' you kept the mare in. They didn't have any female company an' went out lookin' for it. Simple."

"I guess you're right," I said sheepishly. I was quite embarrassed. "I suppose the black mare doesn't get a chance to be a jingle horse in the future."

"Yep, you keep the mare in an' the geldings will stray. But turn her out every night, an' the geldings will stay with her."

I trailed the horses home without incident, but quietly cussed myself all the way. I should have known better!

"Someday," I said to myself, "I'll be able to laugh at this, but not today!"

Now, I can laugh at it, but I can't tell the story without still feeling some embarrassment.

How to Tell When a Cowboy is Lying

[The story is in regular type; what actually happened is in italics. As you can see, not everything a cowboy says is a lie.]

It was a cold, windy day and we had a long way to go. I dreaded a long horseback ride looking for a lost hunting horse in the cold wind. With the wind chill, I thought it was probably around ten degrees below zero, so this wasn't going to be a spring picnic. But one of our horses had gotten lost and he needed to be found, so Jeff and I were headed out.

Actually, it wasn't too bad in the cab of the truck with the heater on. I really felt sorry for our horses back in the trailer. It was really cold for them. I did dread getting into those cold saddles on a day like today. But we did have about 75 miles to go before we had to unload and start riding to look for our lost horse. That's when I dreaded leaving the warmth of the truck.

When we got to Walden, Colorado, we stopped at the sheriff's office to ask if any loose horses had been spotted in the area. We left our horses outside and entered the building. It was a relief to get inside and out of the wind.

I was really hoping someone had found Joe, our missing horse, because I really didn't want to do any riding on a day like this. It was nice in the heated building; I had gotten chilled just walking from the truck to the office.

The sheriff indicated that a stray horse had been spotted about 30 miles away, up by the Wyoming state line. Bundled up to stay warm, we left the confines of the jail and headed back to the horses to resume our hunt. As we left, I offered to leave Jeff as security just in case we picked up the wrong horse. The sheriff declined, but had given us directions on how to get to the house of the person who spotted the horse.

According to the sheriff, a stray horse had been caught up by Mountain Home, Wyoming. He was in a pasture close to the guy's house that had caught him. I did volunteer to leave Jeff as security for future crimes I might commit, but the sheriff declined. The cab of the truck was still warm when we got in to continue our hunt.

As we continued riding, we were constantly on the lookout to spot Joe. Every time we saw a little herd of horses, we had to check it out to make sure Joe wasn't with them. After what seemed like hours, we arrived at the house we were looking for.

We did see some horses along the way. But a quick look over with the binoculars indicated Joe wasn't present. It was a long slow, drive up the bumpy dirt road to the house we were looking for.

We couldn't see any horses close, but did see one quite a ways away. Bracing up for the wind we headed out to see if this horse was the one we were looking for.

Actually, Joe was standing about a hundred yards away, in the corner of a pasture. Jeff grabbed a nosebag full of grain and I grabbed a halter and we walked to the horse. He knew what a nosebag was and approached us eagerly.

RLOREN SCHMIDT

The horse we had seen was Joe. I got a loop on him and we started back. We still had a long way to go to get home, and for a good part of the trip we were headed into the wind.

I flipped the lead rope over Joe's neck as Jeff slipped the nosebag on. We still had a long way to go to get home. Going home was a little slower as we were headed into the wind and we had an extra horse in the trailer. But we did have a good heater in the truck.

We got back to the stables and I limped out of the truck to unsaddle my horse and turn him loose. It had been a cold, hard day.

It had been a cold, hard day, and I did limp turning my horse loose, not because I got froze in the saddle, I just got stiff sitting in the truck all day!

Other Books by Stu Campbell

Horsing Around a Lot

Horsing Around the Dudes

Humor Around Horses

You Can't Be Serious!

R. Loren Schmidt

by Etienne "A-10" Etcheverry
Semi-world famous cowboy cartoonist

How do you describe Loren Schmidt and his art in a few sentences, when it would really take a volume or two. I've been around Loren for the better part of a decade and a half. This artist/gentleman never ceases to amaze me with his unlimited artistic talent in almost any medium—with pen, pencil, brush, and bold colors, he captures the spirit and essence of the New West.

Loren Schmidt is a real artist in every sense of the word, and his talent is not confined to the studio. He is a cowboy, horse trainer, ex-saddle bronc rider/rodeo pickup man, teacher, critic, mentor, and a true friend.